All Aboard!

By Pamela Chanko

ISBN: 978-1-338-88864-5

Editor: Liza Charlesworth
Art Director: Tannaz Fassihi; Designer: Tanya Chernyak
Photos ©: 4: Vladimir Fomin/Dreamstime; 6: LIVINUS/Getty Images; 7: Imel9000/Getty Images; 8: Arjo Van Timmeren / EyeEm/Getty Images. All other photos © Shutterstock.com.

SCHOLASTIC INC.

You can ride on a train.
All aboard!

You can fly on a plane.
All aboard!

You can ride on a bus.
All aboard!

You can sail on a boat.
All aboard!

You can ride on a trolley.
All aboard!

You can float in a balloon.
All aboard!

You can ride on a merry-go-round.
All aboard!